# THE TOP TEN CLASSICAL PIECES EVERY **BEGINNER** PIANIST SHOULD **LEARN**

# THE TOP TEN CLASSICAL PIECES EVERY **BEGINNER** PIANIST SHOULD LEARN

**WISE PUBLICATIONS**
part of The Music Sales Group
London / New York / Paris / Sydney / Copenhagen / Berlin / Madrid / Hong Kong / Tokyo

Published by
Wise Publications
14-15 Berners Street,
London W1T 3LJ, UK.

Exclusive Distributors:
Music Sales Limited
Distribution Centre, Newmarket Road,
Bury St Edmunds, Suffolk IP33 3YB, UK.
Music Sales Corporation
180 Madison Avenue, 24th Floor,
New York NY 10016, USA.
Music Sales Pty Limited
Level 4, Lisgar House,
30-32 Carrington Street,
Sydney, NSW 2000 Australia.

Order No. AM1012231
ISBN 978-1-78558-398-8

Compiled by Naomi Cook.
Notes written by Sandy Burnett.

Photos courtesy of:
Page 14: The Print Collector/Print Collector/Getty Images
Page 18: Gabriel Hackett/Archive Photos/Getty Images
Page 20: Ann Ronan Pictures/Print Collector/Getty Images
Page 26: The Print Collector/Print Collector/Getty Images
Page 30: Hulton Archive/Getty Images
Page 34: Portrait Maurice J. Ravel (1875-1937), French composer.  Photo ca. 1915. Author: Bettmann
Page 36: Leemage/UIG via Getty Images
Page 40: Christie Goodwin/Redferns via Getty Images
Page 45: Fotolia
Page 46: DeAgostini/Getty Images

Printed in the EU.

www.musicsales.com

# THE GRAND STAFF

Music for the piano or keyboard is usually written on a **grand staff** – two staves joined by a **brace**.

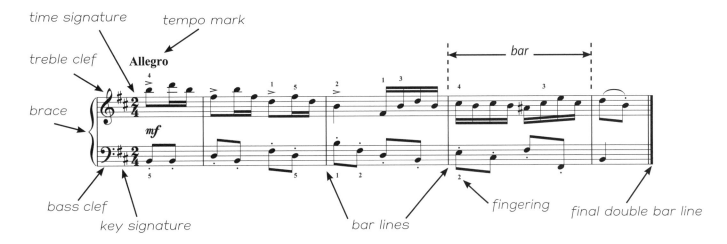

Notes on the upper stave, headed by the **treble clef** (or *G clef*), are usually played by the right hand.

Notes on the lower stave, headed by the **bass clef** (or *F clef*), are usually played by the left hand.

The music is divided by **bar lines** into **bars**. Usually, each bar contains the same number of beats (counts), as indicated by the **time signature** at the beginning of the music.

## CLEFS

 The right hand usually plays music written in the **treble clef.**

This is also called the *G clef* because it spirals around the line on which the note G above Middle C is written.

 The left hand usually plays music written in the **bass clef.**

This is also called the *F clef* because there are two dots either side of the line on which the note F below Middle C is written.

## NOTES VALUES AND RESTS

The note value tells you the duration of a note–how many beats it lasts. When read in sequence, note values show the rhythm of the music.

Each has its own rest, which indicates a silence for the equivalent duration.

| symbol | name | duration | rest |
|---|---|---|---|
| o | semibreve | 4 beats | ▬ |
| ♩ or ⌐ | minim | 2 beats | ▬ |
| ♩ or ⌐ | crotchet | 1 beat | 𝄽 |
| ♪ or ♭ | quaver | ½ beat | 𝄾 |
| ♬ or ♭ | semiquaver | ¼ beat | 𝄿 |

## SHARPS, FLATS AND NATURALS

♯ A **sharp** sign raises the pitch of a note by a semitone to the very next key on the right.

♭ A **flat** sign lowers the pitch of a note by a semitone to the very next key on the left.

♮ A **natural** sign cancels the effect of a sharp or a flat, representing the unaltered pitch.

A **key signature** is written at the start of each line of music. It tells us which notes should be played as sharps or flats and saves writing a ♯ or sign ♭ every time these notes appear.

## TIME SIGNATURES

The **time signature** appears after the key signature at the beginning of the music.

The *upper figure* shows the number of beats in each bar and the *lower figure* tells us what note duration gets one beat.

**4/4** or **C** = four crotchet beats per bar
*(also called common time)*

**3/4** = three crotchet beats per bar

**2/4** = two crotchet beats per bar

**2/2** or **₵** = two minim beats per bar
*(also called cut common time)*

**6/8** = six quaver beats per bar

**12/8** = twelve quaver beats per bar

## OTHER MUSICAL SIGNS

‖ A **double bar line** marks the beginning of a new section of music.

‖ A **final double bar line** marks the end of a piece.

A **slur** is a curved line, over or under a group of notes, indicating that they should be played smoothly (*legato*).

A **tie** is a curved line, connecting two consecutive notes of the same pitch—only the first should be played and then held for the combined value of both notes.

A **staccato** dot, above or below a note, indicates that the note should be played as short and detached.

An **accent** mark, above or below a note, indicates that it should be emphasized by playing it louder than the general dynamic.

A **fermata** (or **pause**) indicates that the note should be held for longer than its written duration.

## FINGERING NUMBERS

Your fingers are given numbers from 1 to 5, starting with the thumbs and numbering outwards.

Fingering is sometimes written above or below notes to help you move your hands around the keyboard efficiently.

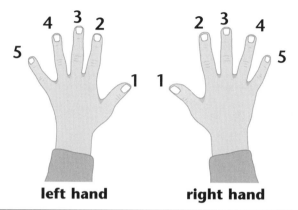

**left hand**          **right hand**

## DYNAMICS

A **dynamic mark** tells you how loudly or softly to play.

| | | |
|---|---|---|
| *pp* | **pianissimo** | very soft |
| *p* | **piano** | soft |
| *mp* | **mezzo piano** | moderately soft |
| *mf* | **mezzo forte** | moderately loud |
| *f* | **forte** | loud |
| *ff* | **fortissimo** | very loud |
| ◁ | **crescendo** *cresc.* | gradually getting louder |
| ▷ | **diminuendo** *dim.* | gradually getting softer |

## REPEAT SIGNS AND OTHER NAVIGATION MARKS

:‖ This is an end **repeat sign,** which tells you to repeat back from the beginning, or from the start repeat: ‖:

|1.    |2.    **First-** and **second-time bars** are used to indicate passages in a repeated section that are only performed on certain playings.

**D.C.** *(Da Capo)* tells you to repeat from the beginning.

**D.C. al Fine** *(Da Capo al Fine)* tells you to repeat from the beginning to the end, or up to **Fine**.

**D.S.** *(Dal Segno)* tells you to repeat from the sign 𝄋.

**D.S. al Coda** *(Dal Segno al Coda)* tells you to repeat from the sign 𝄋 and then, when you reach **to Coda** ⊕, you should jump to the Coda, marked ⊕ **Coda**.

# KEY SIGNATURES

The key of the music is indicated by the **key signature** at the start of each stave,
just after the clef. It tells you which notes in the music should be played as *sharps* or *flats*.

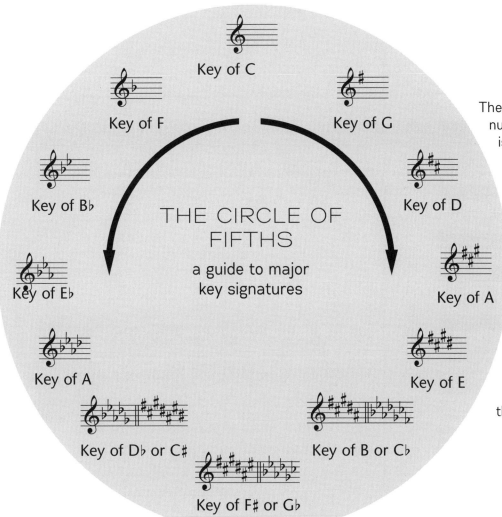

THE CIRCLE OF FIFTHS

a guide to major key signatures

Key of C

Key of F

Key of G

Key of Bb

Key of D

Key of Eb

Key of A

Key of A

Key of E

Key of Db or C#

Key of B or Cb

Key of F# or Gb

The relationship of *major* keys and the number of sharps or flats they each have is shown in this table.

As you pass round the circle in either direction, the key signatures of successive keys include an additional *sharp* or *flat* (depending on your direction of travel).

The keynote, called the **tonic,** of each key is an interval of a *perfect fifth* away from the previous key.

Hence, this circle of keys, which ends where it begins—the key of **C major,** which has no sharps or flats—is called **the circle of fifths.**

---

## MORE ABOUT NOTE VALUES AND RHYTHMS

A **dotted note** lasts for 1½ times its usual duration.

| symbol | name | duration | rest |
|---|---|---|---|
| 𝅗𝅥. or | dotted minim | 3 beats | |
| ♩. or | dotted crotchet | 1½ beats | |
| ♪. or | dotted quaver | ¾ beat | |

A **triplet** is a subdivision of a beat or beats into three notes of equal duration. Using any note value as a unit, three triplet notes divide the duration that two notes would normally occupy into three.

*Triplet quavers*  *divide a crotchet (two quavers) into three.*

*Triplet crotchets*  *divide a minim (two crotchets) into three.*

A **beam** is often used to join note values of a quaver or shorter to show a rhythmic grouping.

The most common grouping is by crotchet beat, which can help you see where the beats of the bar fall.

*rhythm*     *beamed together*

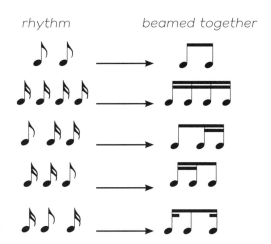

9

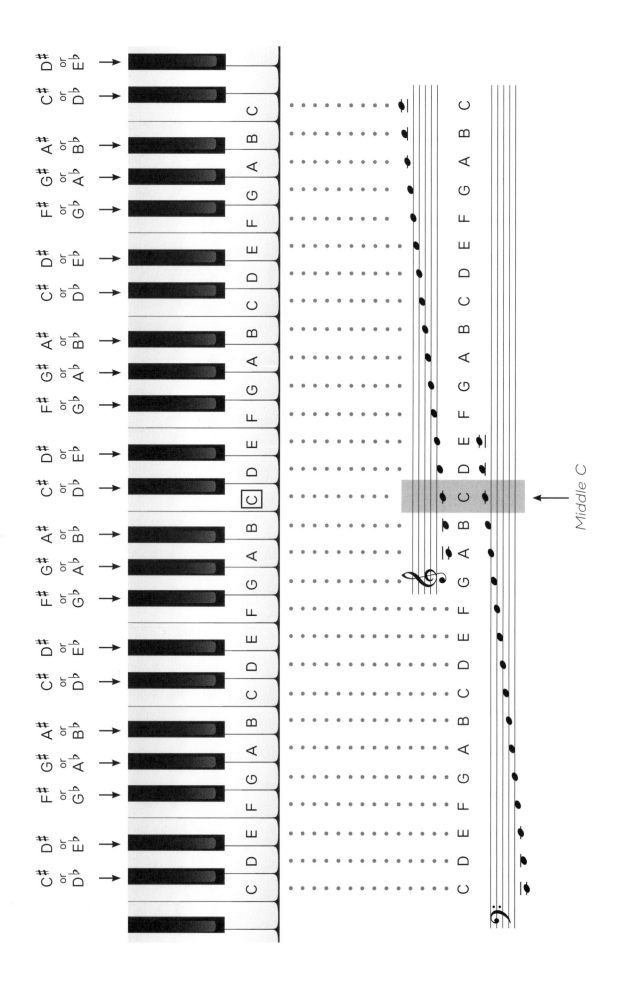

## INTERVALS AND CHORDS

An interval is the distance in pitch between two notes. They are measured and named according to the number of degrees of the scale they comprise. When two notes are played consecutively they form a melodic interval, and when they are sounded together, they form a harmonic interval.

melodic 3rd

harmonic 3rd

melodic 5th

harmonic 5th

A **chord** consists of two or more tones sounded together. A **tonic triad** is a chord comprising three degrees of the scale: *tonic*, *3rd* and *5th*.

## COMMON MAJOR AND MINOR CHORDS

*Major tonic triads*

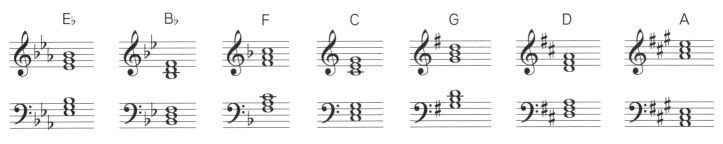

*Minor tonic triads*

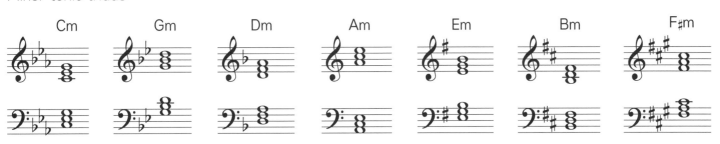

## TEMPO MARKS

A tempo mark at the start of a passage of music tells you what speed to play at. They are often written in Italian.

*Steady tempo*

| slow | Grave | very slowly, dragging |
| | Largo | broadly |
| | Lento | slowly |
| | Adagio slowly, | stately |
| | Andante | at a walking pace |
| | Moderato | moderately |
| | Allegro fast, | brightly |
| | Vivace | lively |
| | Presto | very fast |
| fast | Prestissimo | faster than Presto |

*A change of tempo*

| ritardando (rit.) | gradually getting slower |
| rallentando (rall.) | gradually getting slower |
| poco rit. | getting a little slower |
| allargando | getting broader, slowing |
| meno mosso | less movement, slower |
| | |
| accelerando (accel.) | gradually getting faster |
| più mosso | more movement, faster |
| | |
| a tempo | resume original tempo |

## METRONOME MARKS

A metronome mark may be written at the start of the music to show the precise speed at which it should be played, for example, tells you that there are 72 crotchet beats per minute.

♩ = 72

# WARM-UP EXERCISES

Before you play the piano or keyboard, just like before you do physical exercise, it's important to warm up–this will get your finger coordination working nicely.

Here are some fun workouts for each hand separately, and then hands together. Try to play each exercise musically, with an even tone and steady rhythm.

*Warm ups for the right hand only:*

*Warm ups for the left hand only:*

# THE TOP TEN CLASSICAL PIECES EVERY **BEGINNER** PIANIST SHOULD **LEARN**

Hello and welcome to the *Top Ten Classical Pieces Every Beginner Should Learn*. It can be hard to know where to start when it comes to learning your first pieces – which composers should you be looking out for? How do you decide whether the level of difficulty is right for you? Well, look no further!

Our 'top ten' includes what we think are the best classical pieces for beginners, such as works written to inspire young children, like 'The Doll's Complaint' by Franck and Ravel's musical description of Sleeping Beauty; unforgettable tunes by Beethoven and Handel; and simple but effective spiritual pieces from Johann Sebastian Bach and Ludovico Einaudi.

The background notes on each song provide additional insight into some of the most important composers of the last 300 years. So delve in, and enjoy your first steps into the wonderful world of classical piano!

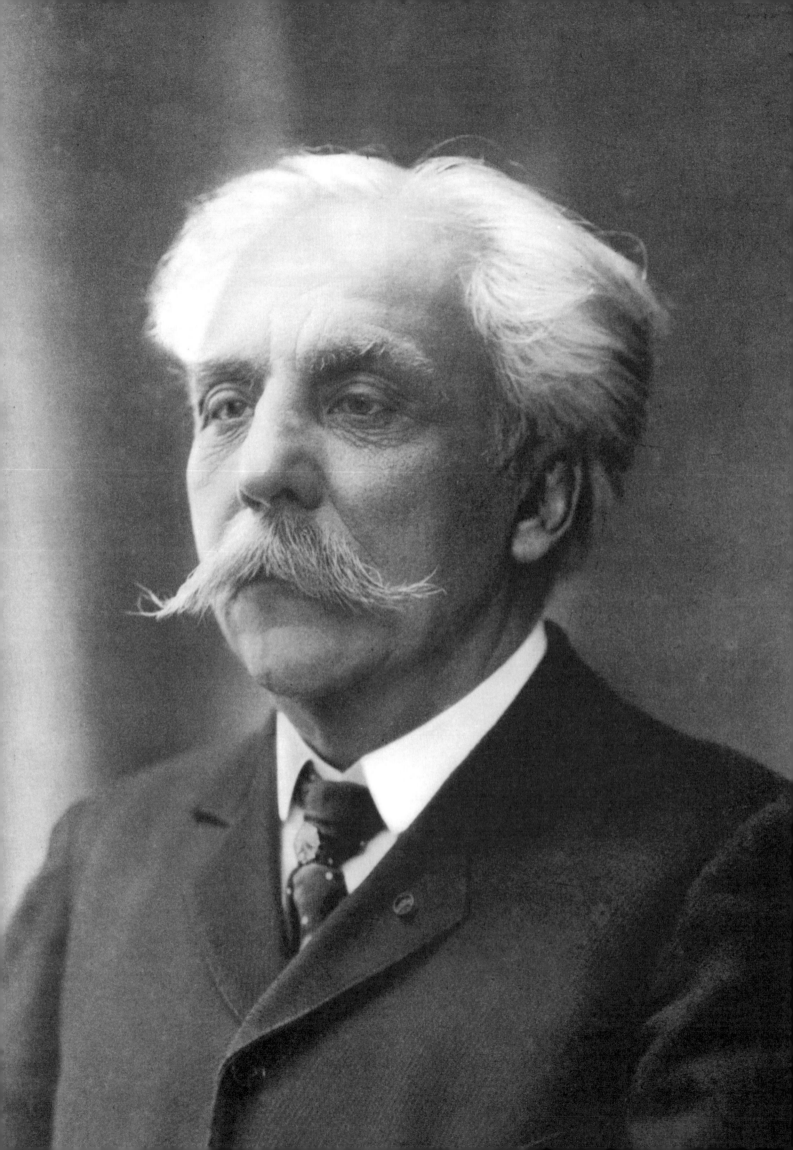

# BERCEUSE
## FROM *DOLLY SUITE*, OP. 56

**COMPOSER:** Gabriel Fauré
**COMPOSED:** 1894

This exquisite French piece is by Gabriel Fauré, who started his journey in music as a church musician, training to become a choirmaster in Paris. He became organist at the famous Madeleine church there, and composed one of the most enduring Requiem settings of all. But Fauré was also quite at home in the city's fashionable salons of the 1890s; he rubbed shoulders there with everyone from well-known socialites such as the Princess Edmond de Polignac to the author Marcel Proust, who said Fauré's music intoxicated him.

Fauré wrote his *Dolly Suite* for a girl he knew called Hélène; she was the daughter of Emma Bardac, an amateur soprano who was Fauré's lover at the time. Everything about this piece is easy-going, from the tempo marking '*andantino moderato*' to the musical language of the piece itself. In the left hand, Fauré alternates two chords in every bar to create a musical image of a baby's cradle being rocked; while in the right, the memorable melody is simple, with long phrase marks indicating that pianists should keep the tune flowing, as though it's a voice line. Not for nothing is he renowned as the greatest French song composer there's ever been!

# BERCEUSE

FROM *DOLLY SUITE*, OP. 56

Gabriel Fauré

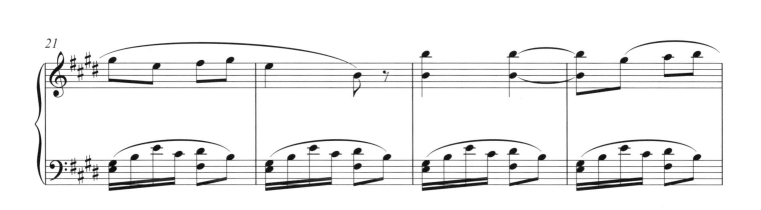

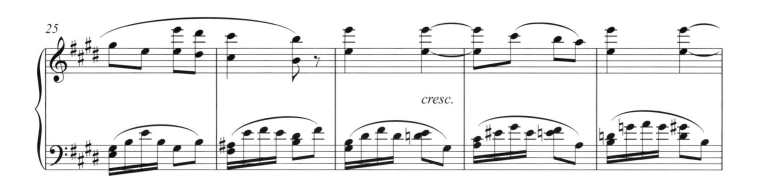

# FUGUE
## FROM *FIVE MINIATURE PRELUDES AND FUGUES*

**COMPOSER:** Alec Rowley
**COMPOSED:** 1946

Taking its meaning from the Latin word for 'flight', the fugue is one of the central forms of keyboard writing. A main theme is introduced at the start; then other melodic strands join in as the first line continues or 'takes flight'. In some of the greatest examples of fugues for keyboard, by the great Johann Sebastian Bach for example, the intertwining of these melodic lines lead to some fiendish finger-crunching for the performer. Not so in this example by Alec Rowley, an English composer who made a speciality of writing with the needs of amateur performers in mind. If you find his music straightforward to play it's because he knew how to express his ideas economically and clearly – a real talent!

This A minor fugue in two parts is the fourth of his set of five miniature preludes and fugues. The rising main theme lies comfortably under the right and left hands. Note the change in texture from the seventh bar, with the dynamic dropping from *forte to piano*, and the hands descending in a sequence of quavers at close quarters. Try not to get those thumbs tangled up!

# FUGUE

## FROM *FIVE MINIATURE PRELUDES AND FUGUES*

### Composed by Alec Rowley

# FÜR ELISE

**COMPOSER:** Ludwig Van Beethoven
**COMPOSED:** 1810

The high repeated Es and D sharps that begin this work usher in one of the best-loved piano pieces of all, and one that every budding pianist should have in the repertoire. The first page isn't all that tricky, and should lie within the capability of an elementary player; it's the later pages that present a few more challenges as the range of the piece widens. It's categorised as a bagatelle, a form of piece which is light and undemanding, but in structural terms it's really a rondo, with a main A section giving way to episodes B and C, with the main theme returning each time.

As for the story behind the piece, well, it's rich in mystery… Beethoven composed it at the age of forty when he was passionately involved with a lady called Therese Malfatti and on the point of proposing to her. A scholar called Ludwig Nohl found the manuscript and published it 45 years later, saying that it was dedicated to Therese but that her name was misspelt on the title page. But was it really Therese who Beethoven was dedicating it to, or did he have another woman named Elise in mind? Well, that document has gone missing again since, so we'll probably never be any the wiser!

# FÜR ELISE

## Composed by Ludwig Van Beethoven

# THE DOLL'S COMPLAINT

**COMPOSER:** César Franck
**COMPOSED:** 1865

Another charming French piece, this one was written with the express purpose of encouraging a reluctant child to do her piano practise. Gabrielle Oeschger was a twelve-year-old pupil of Franck's who had been told off by her mother for being lazy. Franck, however, took the 'carrot rather than the stick' approach when he heard about this little *contretemps* and said he would write a piece for her called 'the tears of her doll'. He was as good as his word, finishing it that very evening. It's an unusual piece for Franck to have written at all; this is the only piano work he produced in a forty-year period that stretched from his twenties through to his sixties. So, Gabrielle was lucky!

Paying tribute to the classical style of piano writing, Franck underpins his piece with an Alberti bass in the left hand, spelling out the chords in an arpeggio pattern; the words *legato sempre* are key here, to keep the harmonies gentle and flowing. The performing direction for the right hand is important too: *dolce* can mean a line is to be played sweetly, but it's also an indication to bring out the melody in a singing style, and that's what Franck is intending here.

# THE DOLL'S COMPLAINT

César Franck

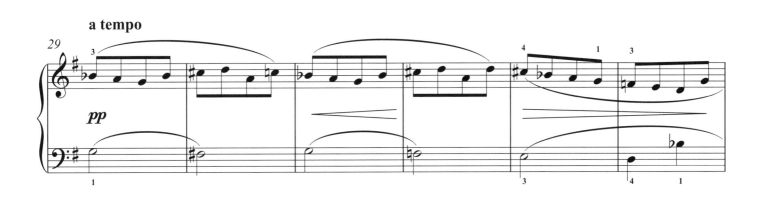

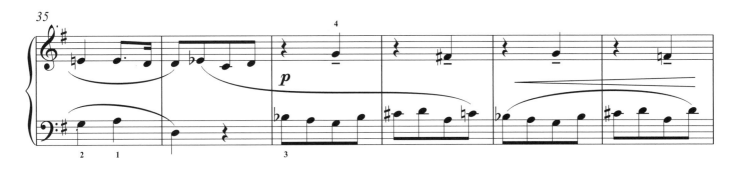

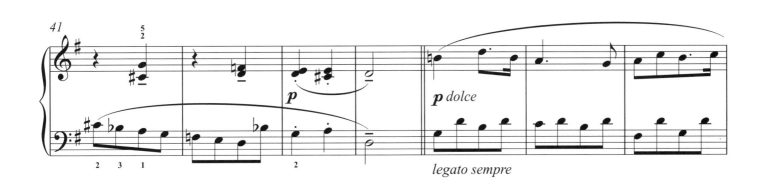

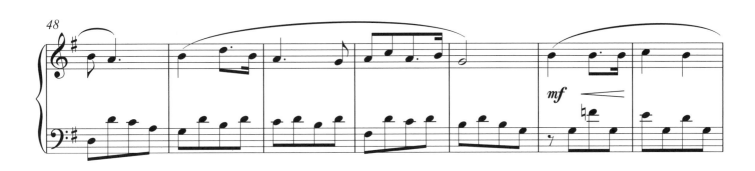

# MELODIE
## FROM *ALBUM FÜR DIE JUGEND*

**COMPOSER:** Robert Schumann
**COMPOSED:** 1848

This touching piece dates from the summer months of 1849, when the leading German composer Robert Schumann took a break from composing large-scale compositions in order to write the first seven pieces of his *Album Für Die Jugend* (*Album For The Young*) for his daughter Marie, making sure he finished them in time to give them to her on her seventh birthday. A touching tribute to his oldest daughter, but also one that he felt there was a real need for. Robert Schumann believed there was a lack of decent teaching material for budding young piano players, and he set out to put that right with this album, which eventually numbered forty-three pieces, the music gradually becoming harder as the collection progresses.

'Melodie' is the very first piece in the album. The long phrase marks, as well as the performance indication *mässig*, meaning 'moderately', indicate that you should aim for a flowing style of playing; use the accents and *crescendo* and *decrescendo* markings to bring shape to the piece.

It's not only Marie who Schumann immortalised in this piece; the falling five-note theme is one that meant a lot to his wife and Marie's mother, Clara Schumann, herself an outstanding pianist and composer. It's a theme they used to express their deep affection for one another in the course of a life in which love did not always run smooth.

# MELODIE

FROM *ALBUM FÜR DIE JUGEND*

Robert Schumann

# MINUET IN F MAJOR, K2

**COMPOSER:** Wolfgang Amadeus Mozart
**COMPOSED:** 1762

Has there ever been a more astonishing child prodigy in classical music than Wolfgang Amadeus Mozart? Not only did the child seem to possess the amazing ability in his genes but he enjoyed quite a bit of nurture as well; Salzburg, where he grew up, was a leading musical centre of the time and being home schooled along with his sister Nannerl meant that the he was able to hear court musicians rehearsing in their apartment on a regular basis. By the age of four, Mozart was playing little pieces on the piano; by the age of five he was composing pieces of his

own – remarkable works such as this *Minuet*, which his ever-ambitious father wrote down for him.

This light and attractive piece has a 'one in a bar' feel; it's a minuet which really dances! Inventively, the young Mozart takes the shape of the first theme and inverts it from the fifth bar onwards. Later on, when the theme appears for the last time, it is reharmonised and rests on a thought-provoking pause before the final phrase brings the piece to close. Not bad at all for a budding five-year-old composer!

# MINUET IN F MAJOR, K2

Wolfgang Amadeus Mozart

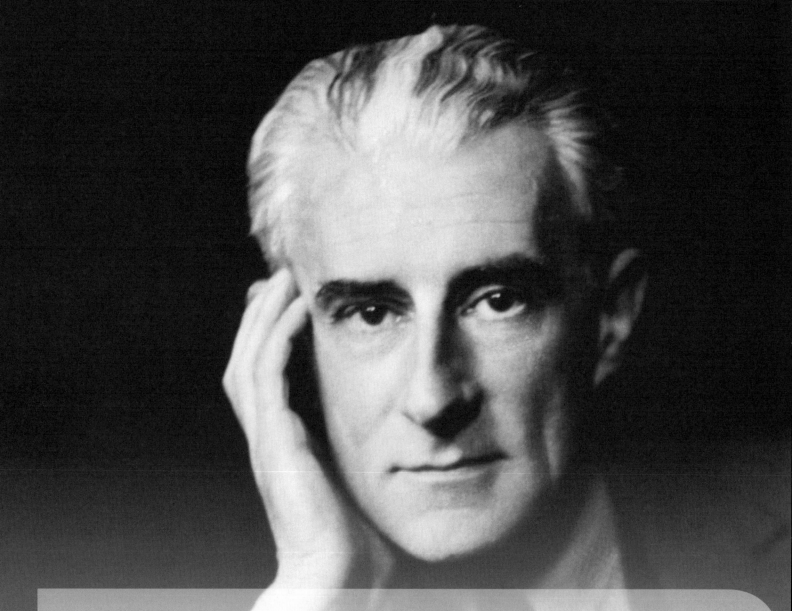

# PAVANE DE LA BELLE AU BOIS DORMANT
## FROM *MA MÈRE L'OYE*

**COMPOSER:** Maurice Ravel
**COMPOSED:** 1910

Whether it's thanks to his stunning 'La Valse' or the much-loved 'Boléro', Maurice Ravel has a justifiable reputation as one of the most sophisticated French composers of all time; his knack of writing spectacular orchestral music has never been bettered. And yet, this ingenious musical craftsman had a great sense of fun and human warmth as well. Although he never married or had offspring of his own, Ravel adored the world of children – he was always happy in their company, and apparently was great at telling fairy tales! That side of the composer is reflected in *Ma Mère L'Oye* (or *Mother Goose Suite*), which sets aspects of five fairy stories to music.

Restful from beginning to end, this movement describes what happens when the Princess pricks her finger on the needle of a spinning wheel: she falls into a deep sleep that lasts a hundred years.

Like the piece from Fauré's *Dolly Suite*, which opens this collection, this movement from *Mother Goose* was originally written for piano duet. Its initial outing would be something ripe for *The X Factor* these days: the suite was first performed by Jeanne Leleu and Genevieve Durony, two remarkable girls who were just six and seven years old at the time.

# PAVANE DE LA BELLE AU BOIS DORMANT

## FROM *MA MÈRE L'OYE*

Maurice Ravel

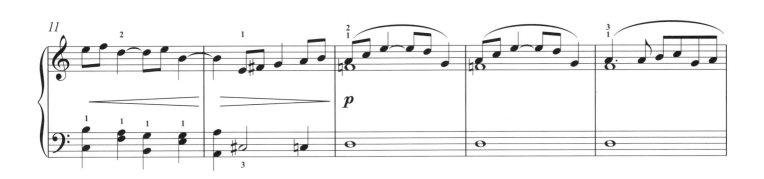

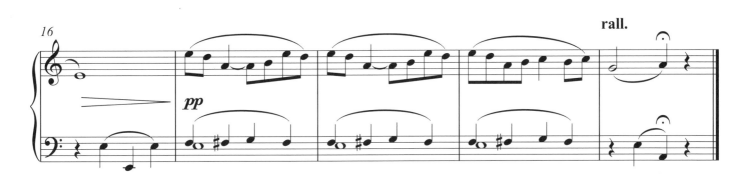

# PRELUDE NO. 1 IN C MAJOR, BWV 846

**COMPOSER:** Johann Sebastian Bach
**COMPOSED:** 1722

One of the most famous keyboard works, this piece kicks off the first book of Bach's 'Well-Tempered Klavier' – a set of twenty-four preludes and fugues in all the available keys. The man himself was an outstanding performer on the organ and harpsichord (the piano itself hadn't quite been invented yet), and when it came to writing music like this, he knew exactly what he was doing. Teaching was uppermost in his mind for this collection – he said that it was 'for the profit and use of musical youth desirous of learning.'

As a curtain raiser for the set, it's deceptively simple; the C major prelude is a piece with no melody, just a free-flowing sequence of semi-quavers in place of rhythm, which left Bach with the basic elements of harmony to work with. Starting and finishing with a pure chord of C major, the piece is really a musical journey that takes us through an ever-changing terrain, weaving through a number of different key areas until the low Gs in the bass line, like the tolling of a bell, herald a return in the closing bars. Although it's a piece which might look simple on the outside, it's a great example of how a masterful composer like Johann Sebastian Bach can do so much with so little.

# PRELUDE NO. 1 IN C MAJOR, BWV 846

Johann Sebastian Bach

# SARABANDE

**COMPOSER:** Ludovico Einaudi
**COMPOSED:** 2012

This Sarabande from the pen of Ludovico Einaudi is a simple yet haunting piece which is a great example of just how attractive his music can be. Born in Turin in 1955, Einaudi was educated in Milan and at Tanglewood in the United States. Since his first album was released in 1988, his music has found a strong connection with audiences all over the world, and he has become one of the biggest-selling and most successful artists around. What's so attractive about his music is that it seems to offer a peaceful refuge from the world we live in; it can evoke strong emotions, but it operates within a framework that balances structure and simplicity. No surprise that Einaudi feels a strong affinity with Johann Sebastian Bach, another composer whose music combined a sense of architecture with profound emotion.

It's easy to take a piece like this one much too fast; reach for a metronome to get the feel of the tempo marking of 'crotchet equals 48', and do bear Einaudi's tempo indication of *Andante calmo* in mind. Nothing should feel rushed or hurried; this is a Sarabande that floats rather than dances.

# SARABANDE

Composed by Ludovico Einaudi

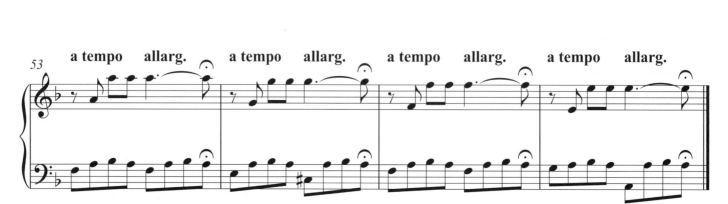

# SARABANDE
## FROM *KEYBOARD SUITE IN D MINOR, HWV 437*

**COMPOSER:** George Frideric Handel
**COMPOSED:** 1703–1706

Georg Friderick Handel was not only an outstanding composer, he was also a man with a fiery temper. Back in the 1720s he famously threatened to throw one of his leading sopranos out of the window of his house in Brook Street, London. That's the kind of rock star behaviour you might more readily associate with someone like Jimi Hendrix, who, as chance would have it, lived in a flat next door many years later in the 1960s. But that hot-headed disposition was just one aspect of his character, as the music writer Charles Burney pointed out: 'He was impetuous, rough, and peremptory in his manners and conversation, but totally devoid of ill-nature or malevolence.'

This Sarabande from his eleventh keyboard suite is a dance movement based on the famous eight-bar Folia chord sequence which countless composers of Handel's day used as a basis for their compositions. We're just presenting the main theme here – Handel used it as the starting point for a whole series of variations, which reflected his own stunning ability as a keyboard improviser. If you feel the urge to improvise a variation of your own on the Sarabande's chords, go for it!

# SARABANDE

## FROM *KEYBOARD SUITE IN D MINOR, HWV 437*

### Composed by George Frideric Handel

123456789

# ALSO AVAILABLE...

| THE TOP TEN CLASSICAL PIANO PIECES EVERY BEGINNER SHOULD LEARN | THE TOP TEN MOST BEAUTIFUL PIECES TO PLAY ON PIANO | THE TOP TEN CHRISTMAS SONGS TO PLAY ON PIANO | THE TOP TEN LOVE SONGS TO PLAY ON PIANO | THE TOP TEN PIANO SONGS OF ALL TIME |
|---|---|---|---|---|
| AM1012231 | AM1012253 | AM1012484 | AM1012275 | AM1012242 |

**THE TOP TEN CLASSICAL PIANO PIECES EVERY BEGINNER SHOULD LEARN** — AM1012231

**BERCEUSE**
from *Dolly Suite*, Op. 56
FAURÉ

**THE DOLL'S COMPLAINT**
FRANCVK

**FÜR ELISE**
BEETHOVEN

**FUGUE**
from *Five Miniature Preludes And Fugues*
ROWLEY

**PAVANE DE LA BELLE AU BOIS DORMANT**
from *Ma Mère L'Oye*
RAVEL

**MELODIE**
from *Album Für Die Jugend*
SCHUMANN

**MINUET IN F MAJOR, K2**
MOZART

**PRELUDE NO. 1 IN C MAJOR, BWV 846**
BACH

**SARABANDE**
from *Keyboard Suite In D minor, HWV 437*
HANDEL

**SARABANDE**
EINAUDI

**THE TOP TEN MOST BEAUTIFUL PIECES TO PLAY ON PIANO** — AM1012253

**ADAGIO FOR STRINGS**
BARBER

**ANDANTE GRAZIOSO**
Theme from *Piano Sonata No. 11 In A Major, K331*
MOZART

**CLAIR DE LUNE**
No. 3 from *Suite Bergamasque*
DEBUSSY

**LASCIA CH'IO PIANGA**
from *Rinaldo, HWV 7*
HANDEL

**MISERERE**
ALLEGRI

**MOONLIGHT SONATA, OP. 27, NO. 2**
BEETHOVEN

**NIMROD**
from *Enigma Variations*, Op. 36
ELGAR

**NOCTURNE IN E♭ MAJOR, OP. 9, NO. 2**
CHOPIN

**NUVOLE BIANCHE**
EINAUDI

**ON THE NATURE OF DAYLIGHT/ WRITTEN ON THE SKY**
from *Shutter Island*
RICHTER

**THE TOP TEN CHRISTMAS SONGS TO PLAY ON PIANO** — AM1012484

**ALL I WANT FOR CHRISTMAS IS YOU**
MARIAH CAREY

**FAIRYTALE OF NEW YORK**
THE POGUES FEAT. KIRSTY MacCOLL

**HAVE YOURSELF A MERRY LITTLE CHRISTMAS**
FRANK SINATRA

**JINGLE BELL ROCK**
BOBBY HELMS

**MERRY XMAS EVERYBODY**
SLADE

**SANTA BABY**
EARTHA KITT

**SANTA CLAUS IS COMIN' TO TOWN**
EDDIE CANTOR

**WALKING IN THE AIR**
Theme from *The Snowman*
PETER AUTY/ALED JONES

**WHITE CHRISTMAS**
BING CROSBY

**WINTER WONDERLAND**
DEAN MARTIN

**THE TOP TEN LOVE SONGS TO PLAY ON PIANO** — AM1012275

**AT LAST**
ETTA JAMES

**CLOSE TO YOU (THEY LONG TO BE)**
THE CARPENTERS

**(EVERYTHING I DO) I DO IT FOR YOU**
BRYAN ADAMS

**THE FIRST TIME EVER I SAW YOUR FACE**
ROBERTA FLACK

**HOW DEEP IS YOUR LOVE**
BEE GEES

**I WILL ALWAYS LOVE YOU**
WHITNEY HOUSTON

**MAKE YOU FEEL MY LOVE**
ADELE

**MY HEART WILL GO ON**
from *Titanic*
CÉLINE DION

**MY IMMORTAL**
EVANESCENCE

**YOUR SONG**
ELTON JOHN

**THE TOP TEN PIANO SONGS OF ALL TIME** — AM1012242

**BRIDGE OVER TROUBLED WATER**
SIMON & GARFUNKEL

**CLOCKS**
COLDPLAY

**DON'T STOP BELIEVIN**
JOURNEY

**LIFE ON MARS?**
DAVID BOWIE

**ORDINARY PEOPLE**
JOHN LEGEND

**SKINNY LOVE**
BIRDY

**SOMEONE LIKE YOU**
ADELE

**SOMEWHERE ONLY WE KNOW**
KEANE

**A THOUSAND MILES**
VANESSA CARLTON

**TINY DANCER**
ELTON JOHN

| THE TOP TEN CONTEMPORARY CLASSICAL PIECES TO PLAY ON PIANO | THE TOP TEN MOST CALMING SONGS TO PLAY ON PIANO | THE TOP TEN FILM THEMES TO PLAY ON PIANO | THE TOP TEN POP SONGS EVERY BEGINNER PIANIST SHOULD LEARN | THE TOP TEN JAZZ SONGS TO PLAY ON PIANO |
|---|---|---|---|---|
| AM1012286 | AM1012319 | AM1012264 | AM1012297 | AM1012308 |